For my favorite *Giants* fan, my husband, and our little *Giants* fans, Addison and Bodie. To my parents for always supporting their children's dreams.

- Julie

www.mascotbooks.com

7th Inning Stretch

For more information, please contact:
Mascot Books
560 Herndon Parkway #120
Herndon, VA 20170
info@mascotbooks.com

CPSIA Code: PRT1213A
ISBN-10: 162086536X
ISBN-13: 9781620865361

Printed in the United States

by Julie Brennan

We're dressed in our gear.
We have our gloves and our hats.
We cannot wait to see
who is going to come up to bat!

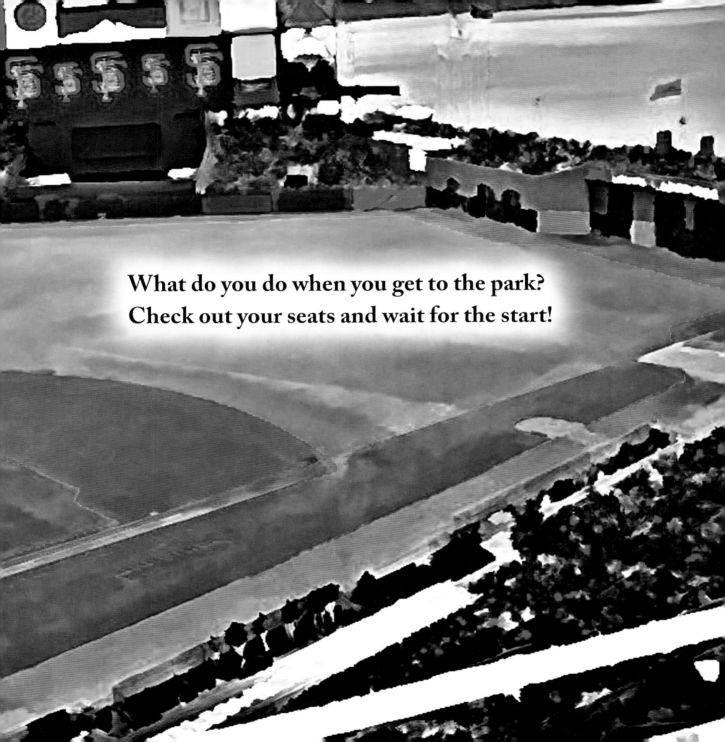

What do you do when you get to the park?
Check out your seats and wait for the start!

The bottom of the 1st is already here,
"Let's go boys!" We're ready to stand up and cheer!

The top of the 5th and we're down by two.
Should we go get a snack or watch the mound
to see what the pitcher will do?

It's the middle of the 7th; do you know what that means?
Let's stretch our legs, it's time to sing…

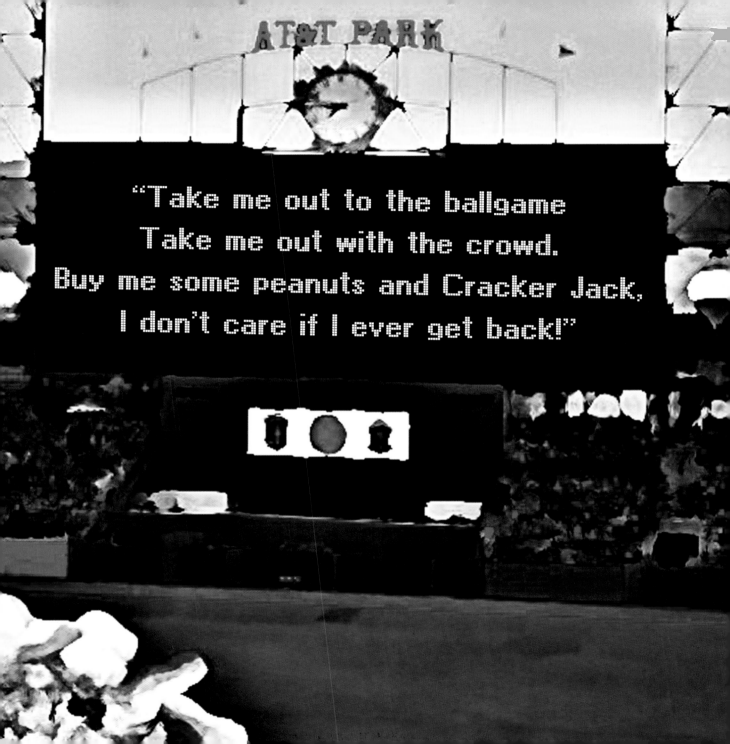

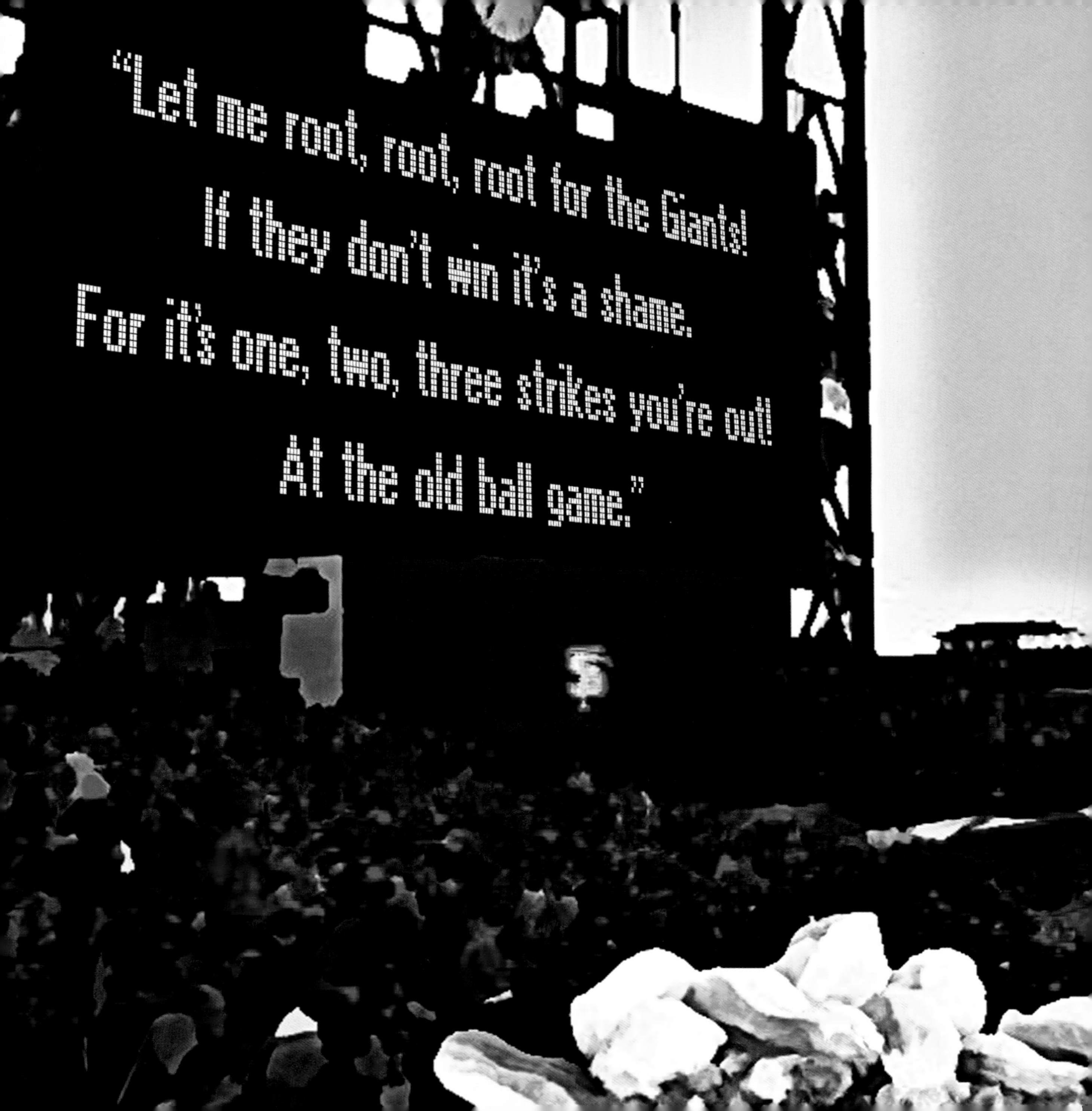
"Let me root, root, root for the Giants!
If they don't win it's a shame.
For it's one, two, three strikes you're out!
At the old ball game."

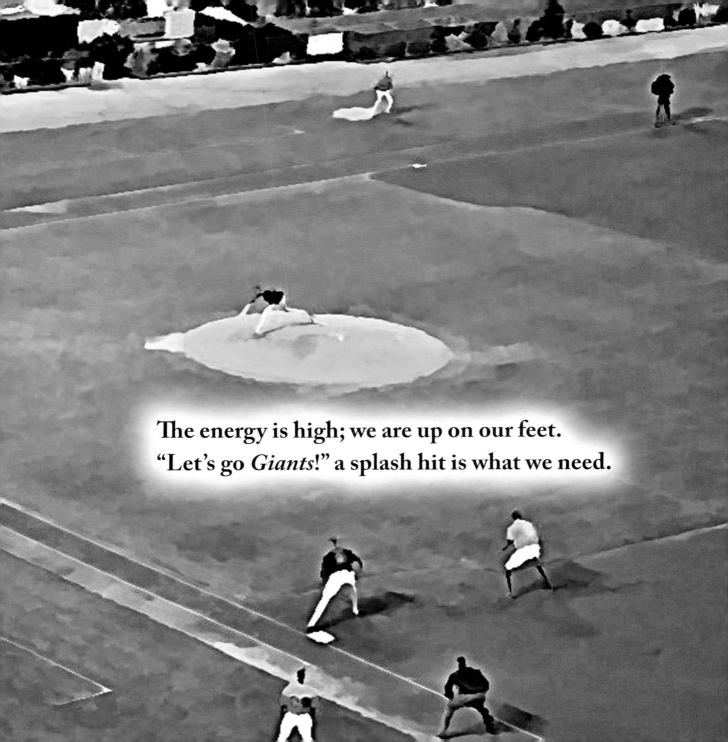

The energy is high; we are up on our feet.
"Let's go *Giants*!" a splash hit is what we need.

The ball is thrown and then hit with a whack!
We are sure that ball will go "splash!" and never come back.

The top of the 9th, can we hold this lead?
Yes! The *Giants* win! The *Giants* win!
What a great game indeed!

As we start to head out,
I can't help but remember that familiar tune:
"Take Me Out To The Ballgame…" and I smile
because I know we will be back soon!

Did you know?

- The team originated in 1883 as the New York Gothams
- While in New York the team won 5 *World Series* Championships
- In 1958 the *New York Giants* moved to San Francisco, the same year the *Brooklyn Dodgers* moved to Los Angeles
- The *San Francisco Giants* played at Seal Stadium and Candlestick Park before calling AT&T Park (formally Pacific Bell Park) their home in 2000
- AT&T Park can hold 41,503 fans

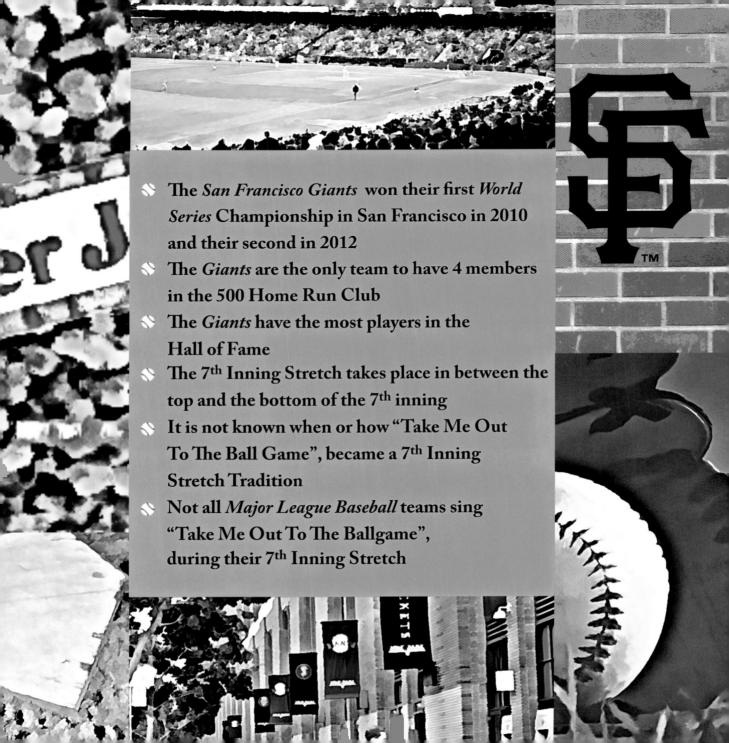

- The *San Francisco Giants* won their first *World Series* Championship in San Francisco in 2010 and their second in 2012
- The *Giants* are the only team to have 4 members in the 500 Home Run Club
- The *Giants* have the most players in the Hall of Fame
- The 7th Inning Stretch takes place in between the top and the bottom of the 7th inning
- It is not known when or how "Take Me Out To The Ball Game", became a 7th Inning Stretch Tradition
- Not all *Major League Baseball* teams sing "Take Me Out To The Ballgame", during their 7th Inning Stretch

About the Author

Julie Brennan didn't always love baseball. It was not until she lived in New Hampshire, where the rivalry of the *Boston Red Sox* and *New York Yankees* ran deep, that she truly understood and appreciated the game. She now loves watching the *San Francisco Giants* with her husband and two children.